THE UGLY DUCKLING

duck

farm

field

ducks

geese

chickens

nest

ducklings

water

goose

wood

cottage

pool

reeds

swans

path

These are illustrations of some of the characters and things from the book. Let your listeners See and Say them, get to know them, before you read the story. Then, as you read, pause and point to each picture in the text, letting the child supply the illustrated word. Young children love to follow stories in this way and it gives them a first exercise in the movement of reading.

A little brown 🦆 lived on a farm near a river. There was a small green 🟫 where the 🦆🦆 and 🦆 and 🐓 had their homes. But when it was time for the brown 🦆 to lay her 🥚 she made a 🪹 by the river and laid the 🥚 there. Then she tucked her wings around them and waited for her 🦆🦆 to come.

Soon the  cracked open and out came the . The brown was very proud of them and when they were strong enough, she took them to swim on the .

They swam very well but the farm and the , who were trotting by the , laughed and laughed at them.

Grandfather 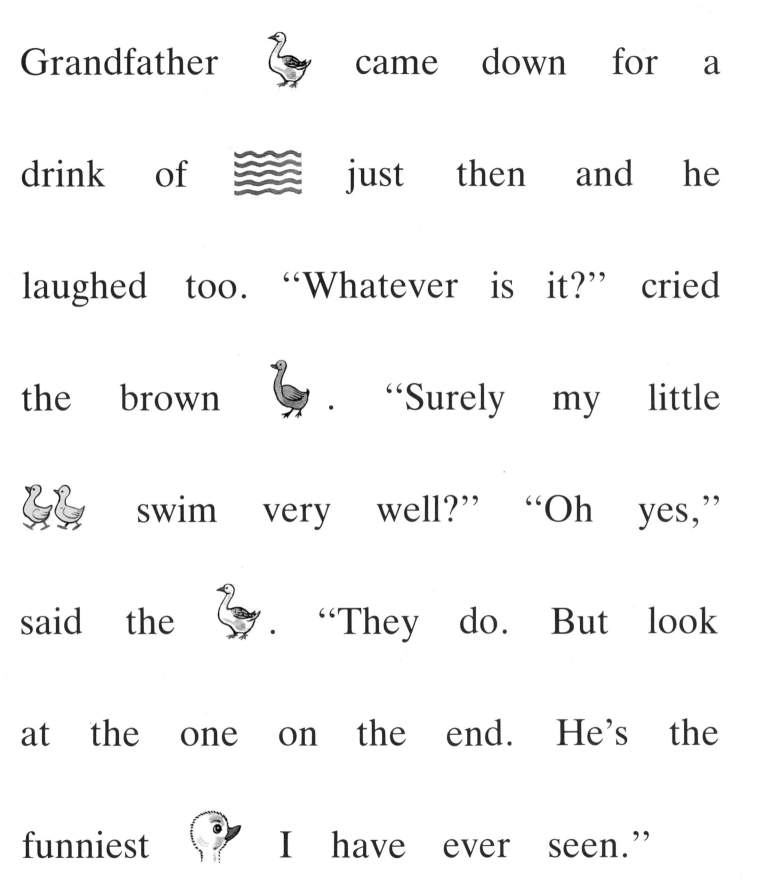 came down for a
drink of 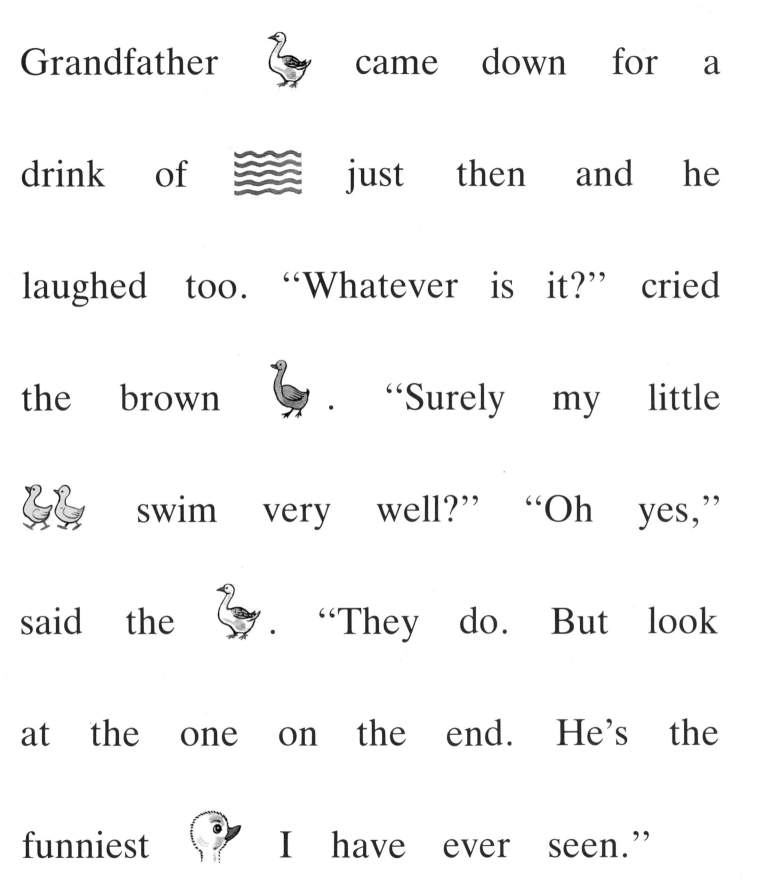 just then and he
laughed too. "Whatever is it?" cried
the brown 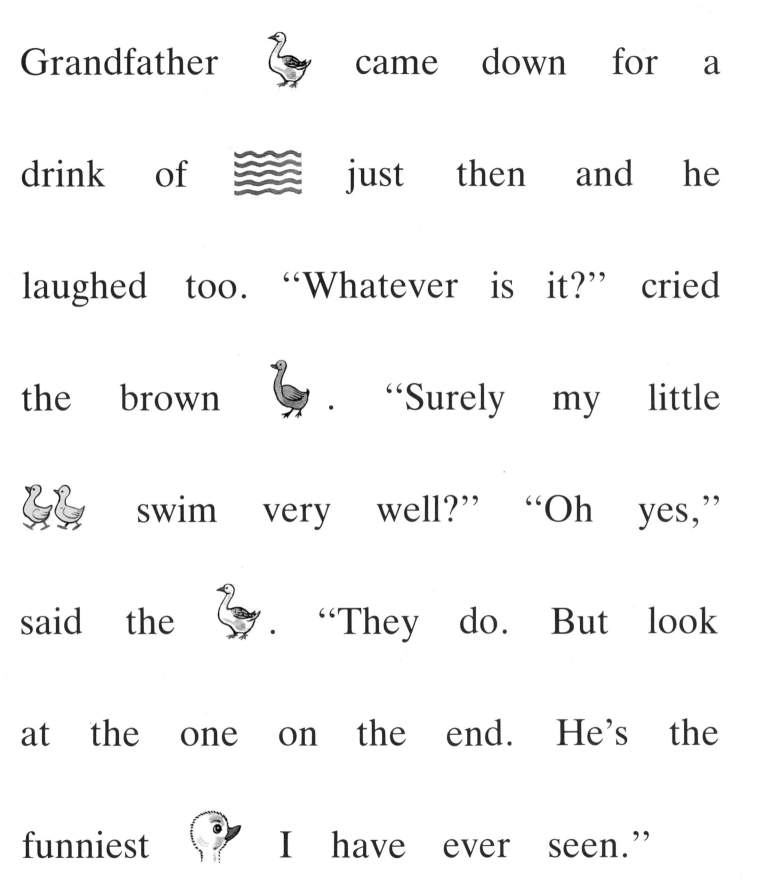. "Surely my little
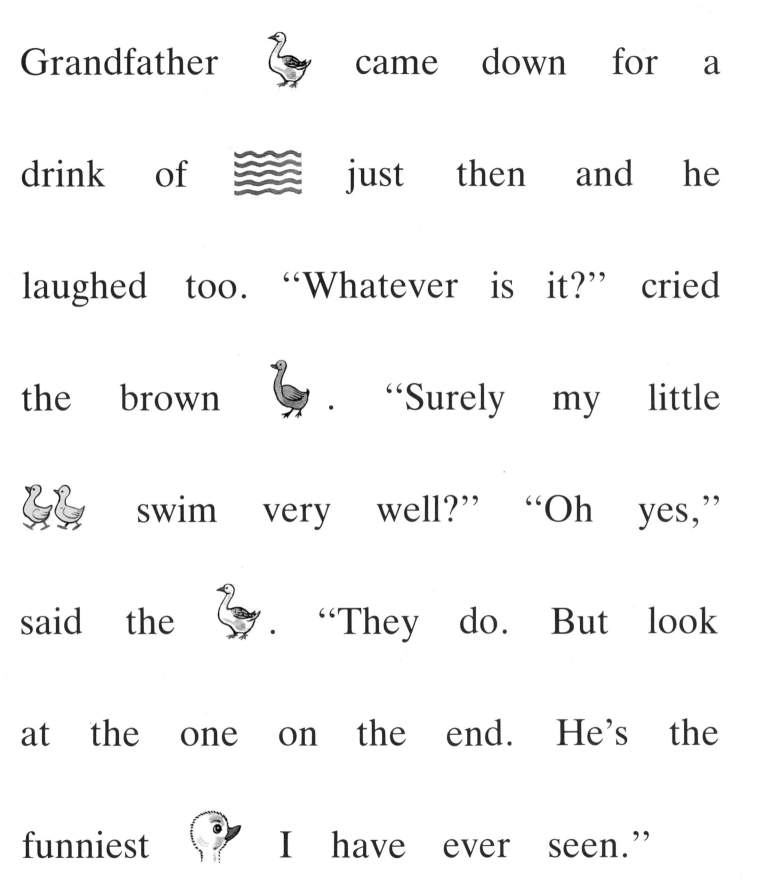 swim very well?" "Oh yes,"
said the 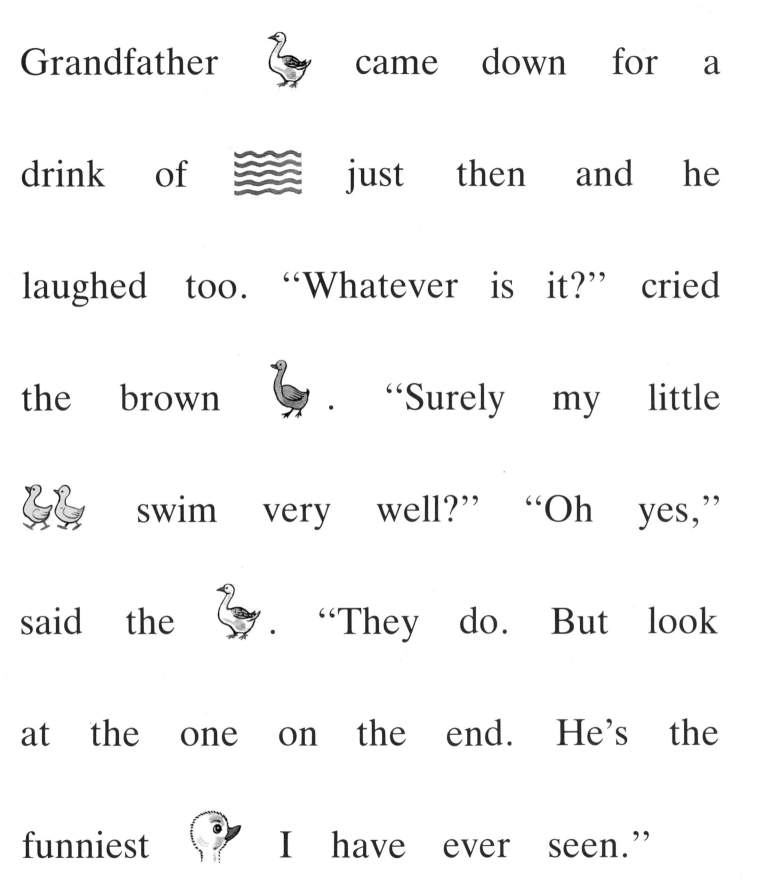. "They do. But look
at the one on the end. He's the
funniest 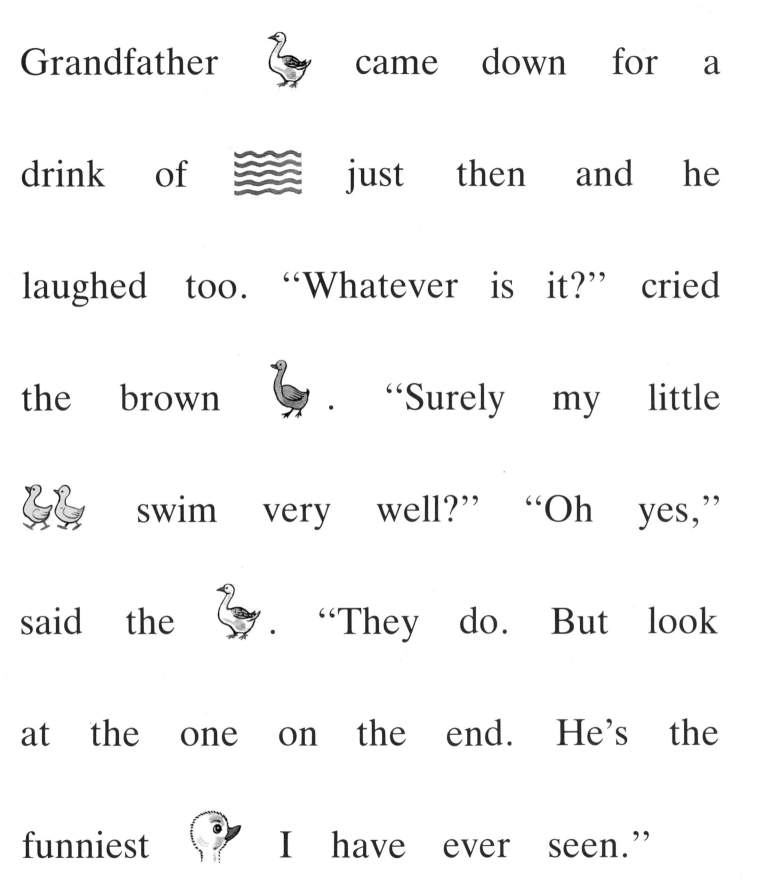 I have ever seen."

The brown  took her family
back to the small green
but all the and began
to laugh too.

As the days went by, the  and the were most unkind to the . So he said, "I will go away, Mother," and he sadly left the forever.

Soon he came to a where and lived. The soon met some wild there. They were not unkind to him. They were quite friendly. But one day they all heard barking very loudly . "Hunters!" cried the . "Fly! Fly!" And they flew away over the .

The  wings were too young to fly, so he ran away from the as fast as he could.

He went on through the until it was almost night. Then he saw a shining from a window. The went nearer and he found that the had been left open. He crept through into the warm kitchen and fell fast asleep. An old lived there and she was very kind to him.

But the old  had a pet 🐱 and a pet 🐔. They were not at all pleased to find the 🦆 in their home and they began to make fun of him.

So the  went back to the woods and found a quiet place beside a ◎, where he could catch 🐟 and sleep among the 🌿

One evening he saw some lovely  on the ∼∼∼ but they soon spread their wings and flew away. The 🐤 had never seen 🦢 before. He was sad to see them go.

After that he lived alone among the  until winter. It became so cold the froze hard and the was caught in its icy grip.

Then a  came by. He broke the ice and took the  home. Beside the warm  he soon felt better but the  frightened him.

They only wanted to play but the fluttered away through an open and ran off down the garden .

He went back to the beside the . But now he found a dry place among some ferns and lived there, with to eat, and sheltered by the until spring came.

Then one day the  found the ☼ was shining. 🐦 were singing. He spread his wings, and suddenly he was flying – flying away over the 🌳🌳 to green fields beyond.

The  came down to rest on a lake of shining ~~~~, where 🦢 were swimming. One came gliding towards him.

The  shyly bent his head, looking down at the shining ~~~. He saw himself in it, as in a ⊐. But he looked like a 🦢!

Other  came closer, gliding over the ~~~~~. "What a handsome young 🦢!" they said. "Do come and join us."